GENERAL
BILLYCOCK'S
PIGS

STORY
AND
PICTURES
BY

JOAN BALFOUR
PAYNE

Weekly Reader Children's Book Club

presents

GENERAL BILLYCOCK'S PIGS

HASTINGS HOUSE, PUBLISHERS
New York

A WORD ABOUT THIS BOOK

Eastern Tennessee, where this story takes place, is a country of heavily-forested mountains and rich, lovely valleys. Not two hundred years ago it belonged to the Indians, and to the wild animals: the mountain cat, the deer, and the bear.

Soon after the American Revolution, people from the first thirteen states, from Virginia and the Carolinas especially, began pouring into the newly-opened wilderness of Tennessee. They came by horseback and wagon, by flatboat where the rivers were wide and deep enough, and on foot. They brought their livestock with them—pigs, cows, and horses. Their chickens and geese cackled and squawked from crates atop the lurching wagons on the wilderness roads. Their fiddles and their voices sounded bravely on the wilderness air.

These people were farmers and woodsmen, craftsmen, doctors, musicians, teachers, and preachers. Some were rascals, thieves, and highwaymen, wanted for their crimes farther east. Many had been soldiers and a few, like General Billycock, were generals.

They cleared farms in the green valleys and built log cabins on the mountainsides, taverns on the new stage roads, and bustling settlements by the fords of the shining rivers. A few, like General Billycock, built great stone houses and called them by proud names such as Cragfont, which is a real house and still stands today as it stood in 1800.

As the roads spread and pushed back the wilderness, the drovers came, too, with their fabulous herds of cattle and hogs. There are still many legends in the mountains of Tennessee about the great drives.

Perhaps General Billycock's pigs were just a band of "escapees" from a drover's herd. Or perhaps they were something quite different, indeed, as the wise old Indian shaman told the General's daughter. Read and see what you think. . . .

JOAN BALFOUR PAYNE

THERE WAS ONCE a general. His name was General Billycock and oh, what a temper he had! He fought against the
Indians and he fought against the Redcoats. When he got mad
he frightened his whole army from the officers right on down
to the lowliest private. He frightened the Indians and the Redcoats, too.

When all the Redcoats had sailed back to where they came
from and the Indians had settled down, General Billycock came
west over the Cumberland Mountains and built himself a fine
big square stone house on a hill looking over the wide, rolling
waters of the Tennessee River.

Now that he was no longer at the head of an army, when the General got mad he frightened his wife, his six big stout sons, the servants, and the neighbors. The hounds ran under the house and the cats ran up the trees. Even the bears and wolves and panthers in the forest round about got scared and hid. The only creatures for miles who weren't at all bothered by General Billycock's temper were his young daughter, Betsy, and his big old charger Cannonball.

Cannonball was a red roan with a rolling eye and a low-laid ear. He wasn't scared of man or beast, thunder or lightning, and he had carried the General through many a battle. Sometimes Cannonball would step on the General's toe or nip him lightly as he was getting into the saddle, just to show the General that he couldn't frighten *him!*

Betsy had Irish-blue eyes and apple-red cheeks and black curls tied up with cherry ribbons. She was nine years old and, although she loved her father dearly, she thought he was rather silly when he fell into a temper and shouted, so she always laughed at him. Betsy and Cannonball were the only creatures the General never shouted at.

Every morning early General Billycock would rise very quietly before anyone else and ride out to look at his land and his crops. Then he would come galloping back, shouting and roaring and carrying on because his breakfast wasn't ready, or because it was overdone. His wife would cry, his six big stout sons would fall all over themselves, and the cook would burn the hominy and break the crockery. This pleased General Billycock immensely.

8

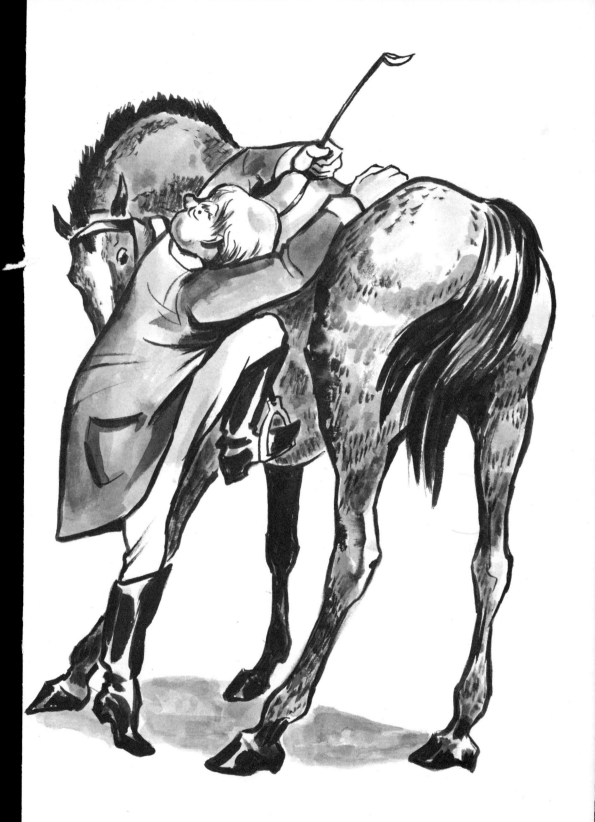

One fine clear morning, just as the eastern sky was growing rosy and the bright morning star was gently fading, General Billycock rode out as usual, having taken great care not to wake anyone. As he rode along, he thought happily of how he was going to upset them all when he got back. He was smiling to himself over this as he reached the edge of his tobacco field—and then, oh! what a bellow he gave, loud even for him!

There lay his beautiful tobacco crop all uprooted and trampled to bits! General Billycock dug his spurs into Cannon-ball's sides—a thing he usually thought about thrice before doing—and away they went over the poor ruined tobacco to the edge of the cornfield.

Now he bellowed twice as loud—they heard him up and down the Tennessee for miles! The beautiful corn that only the evening before had been standing tall and green and silky-tasseled was all uprooted and trampled down! Again General Billycock dug his spurs into Cannonball's sides (he should never have done it!) and away they went over the poor ruined corn to the edge of the potato field.

What the General saw now filled him with such rage that for the first time in his life he couldn't utter a sound. There lay the lovely potato plants all broken and uprooted like the corn and the tobacco. And in the middle of the field, shoveling up dirt and potatoes with their snouts as hard as they could were pigs!

Little pigs and big pigs! In-between-size pigs! Black and rusty-red they were—some all black and some all red. Some were black with red spots, some red with black spots. Their backs rose high to a sharp ridged bone, their curly tails swung round and round, and a more mean and ugly-looking lot could not be imagined.

General Billycock sat trembling on Cannonball, his face growing darker every minute. Finally he found his voice.

"Get off my land, you miserable, thieving swine!" he shouted in a truly terrible manner.

The pigs stopped shoveling and looked up at him slyly out of their little squinty eyes. Then they all went right back to work shoveling up potatoes harder than ever.

Such behavior was unheard of—strong men had been known to faint dead away when General Billycock shouted like that! For the third time that morning the General stuck his spurs into Cannonball's sides. It was an awful mistake. If the General hadn't been in quite such a rage he would have thought better of it. He rose in the stirrups, his riding whip in his right hand raised high above his head. With a completely horrifying bellow he prepared to charge the enemy.

But instead of bounding forward like the good war horse that he was, Cannonball planted both front hoofs solidly, ducked his head, and gave a mighty buck. General Billycock, bellowing, flew skyward and came down again *thud!* sitting right under the untidy snout of the largest pig, a big old black boar!

The pig and General Billycock stared at each other in surprise. "Hoo!" said the pig, dribbling dirt, and he grinned wickedly as only pigs can grin.

12

General Billycock brought his riding whip down hard on the black pig's head.

"You horrid beast!" he rasped, for his voice had been nearly ruined by that last bellow. "What are you doing on my property, spoiling my crops? Get off immediately before I butcher the lot of you and hang you all up in my smokehouse!"

The black pig seemed utterly undisturbed by either the General's voice or the clout on the head. He lowered his snout and began to shovel dirt and potatoes faster than ever.

"Go away! Keep going! You can't stop here! I won't allow it!" panted General Billycock, belaboring the pig with his whip.

The black pig, with a sudden great upward thrust of his snout, uprooted an especially large potato and sent it flying. It hit the General square on the nose. Dirt showered all over the General's clean coat and breeches. With a final insolent toss of his snout, which seemed to say, "We're going but we'll be back!" the pig turned and trotted away to the woods. The rest of the band, looking slyly at the exhausted General, left off their digging and followed him.

By this time General Billycock's family and servants had arrived on the scene, brought by all the noise and the sight of Cannonball galloping riderless home. When they found the General sitting silently in the middle of the ruined potato field, they began to weep and wail and wring their hands—all except Betsy, who was of a very practical nature. She went immediately to her father and said to him, "Dearest Papa, if you are not injured, do kindly get up out of the dirt for you are ruining your new linsey breeches."

When the General tried to get up, however, he found that he had strained his knee, the one that had a bit of shot in it from an old battle. So his six stout sons and the servants had to carry him home, and although he shouted at them as best he could every step of the way, it was plain that his heart was not really in it. Truly, it was hard for an old soldier who had beaten both the Indians and the Redcoats to be bested by pigs!

As soon as he was settled in his great four-poster bed, with his knee bound up, General Billycock directed his six big stout sons to take their blunderbusses and go into the forest in search of the band of pigs. This they did.

Before nightfall they came running and stumbling back, all big stout six of them. Their clothes were torn by briars, their

faces were scratched, and two of them had lost their blunder-busses. They had found the pig tracks and followed them deep into the forest, but the cunning pigs had made a circle around them and then rushed in on them all at once, making horrid noises, and almost frightening the General's sons into fits. At this news General Billycock was furious!

The next day he sent his strongest servants into the forest armed with pitchforks and nets. Before nightfall the servants came running and stumbling back, strong though they were, their clothes and faces scratched and torn by briars. They, too, had found pig tracks which they had followed deep into the forest. Again the cunning pigs had crept around behind and jumped out at them from the underbrush, making horrid noises. Frightened almost into fits, the servants had dropped their pitchforks, got themselves tangled in the nets, and just barely managed to get home again. The General nearly broke a blood vessel, he was so furious.

Every night the pigs visited the fields, spoiling what was left of the crops. When they finished with those, they moved closer to the house itself, rooting up the fine new lawn that was General Billycock's pride. The way things were going, they would soon be in the flower garden itself, ruining the General's wife's flowers and the tender boxwood brought all the way over the mountains from Virginia.

Soon the pigs grew so bold that they came in broad daylight and if anyone made a move to drive them off they would charge, their bristles up on their high, bony backs, their mean, squinty little eyes glowing red, their wicked tusks grinding. Gunshot had no effect on their hides, which were as tough as armor. And of course it was useless to plant new crops, for as fast as they came up the pigs would destroy them.

It was really too much for the General, who was so unused to defeat. He grew weaker and paler and soon was unable to speak much above a whisper. Oh, it was sad to behold him!

One day he sent for his little daughter, Betsy. When she came, she was so pretty in her gown of sprigged muslin and her cherry ribbons that the General almost forgot his troubles.

"Here," he said, patting her hand as she sat beside him on the brightly colored counterpane, "you are the cleverest of my children, far cleverer than any one of your six brothers. You can read and write and cipher much better than they."

Betsy could read and write and cipher better than the General too, but, of course, she did not say so. She only curtsied nicely.

"Now," her father continued, "I have a notice to be sent out through the settlement and I want you to copy it in your very best penmanship." So Betsy curtsied again and ran to get her copybook and quill pen.

This was the notice that Betsy copied out in her very best penmanship with curlicues and flourishes:

To All and Sundry
Be it known
That General Billycock
of this Settlement
Offers a Sizable Reward
in Gold and Silver
to Anyone Who Can Rid
His Property of a
Most Vicious Band
of Pigs!!

This notice was taken by a servant and nailed to a post in the heart of the settlement where all could see it.

The news soon spread. Those who could read—there were not many in those days!—told those who could not of the General's offer, so, in a day or two, from up and down the Tennessee people came on foot and on horseback for miles to rid General Billycock of his affliction.

The first to try was a great yellow-bearded man in buckskin with a long rifle on his arm. He patted the long rifle proudly.

"Ole Lucy, she's a mighty fine piece. I've kilt lions and buffalo with her and shot the war bonnet off an Injun chief!"

General Billycock perked up enough to sit in a wing chair by his window to watch the slaughter.

The pigs were in the turnip patch, rooting and shoveling for all they were worth. The yellow-bearded man knelt down and aimed at the big black boar who was their leader. BANG! went Ole Lucy, the long rifle. The black pig flicked his curly tail and looked up, his ears flapping over his mean, squinty little eyes. Then he went back to work.

The yellow-bearded man loaded Ole Lucy again and BANG! she went. But except for a flick of his tail the pig showed nothing. So it was with the other pigs. Their hides were so tough that even the powerful long rifle had no effect on them.

The yellow-bearded man went away, his head low, and General Billycock went back to bed.

A tall, thin man in homespun with a coonskin cap on his head came next with a couple of fierce-looking hounds which he set loose on the band of pigs.

"Ole Luke and Sadie," he said proudly, "they're a mighty fine pair. I've hunted panthers and bears with 'em and they've never run from ary a critter yet!"

General Billycock perked up enough to sit by the window and watch the chase.

And a chase it was—although not quite as expected. For the hounds' sharp teeth and ferocious baying did not trouble the pigs at all except they seemed annoyed with all the ruckus. They suddenly stopped shoveling and rushed the hounds, grunting and snapping their tusks, their squinty little eyes glowing red. The hounds turned tail, yelping. They ran until they were out of sight, with the band of pigs right behind them. Then the pigs came trotting back, grunting with satisfaction, and commenced rooting and shoveling again.

The tall, thin man in homespun went away after the hounds, his head low, while General Billycock went back to bed.

Then along came an old wizened granny woman who claimed to be a witch.

"I'll make 'em fade away into thin air in no time a-tall," she croaked, and the General found strength to sit by the window, wrapped up in a shawl, to watch the wondrous disappearance. The old granny woman squatted down at the edge of the bean patch where that day the pigs were busily rooting and began to recite spells in a strange tongue. She made curious signs in the direction of the pigs. Nothing happened. The pigs kept right on at their affairs even though the old woman started to dance and jig and wave her arms at them, shrilling magic words. Presently she stubbed her toe on a rock, which caused the pigs to grin wickedly.

At last the old granny woman hobbled away, muttering, and General Billycock went back to bed.

Others came. Traps were tried, but the pigs were too cunning and would not be caught. They even broke the traps. One man appeared dragging a small cannon, but the pigs only moved to a safe distance and then returned to root in the holes made by the cannon balls.

At last a man came with a great basket of poisoned rutabagas and dropped them about the fields.

"Pizen will do it!" he boasted.

The pigs soon appeared and ate up the rutabagas, every single one, then trotted away to the forest. What rejoicing there was! The General looked like a new man. His color, like brick dust, came back to his face and his china-blue eyes gleamed.

The next morning, however, as he was counting the first gold pieces into the poisoner's hand, there came the pigs, all of them, trotting out of the forest as hale as before! They ran about, grunting, as if they were looking for more rutabagas. The would-be poisoner went away, his head low, without the reward, and General Billycock took to his bed.

"I will never get up again," he said to his weeping family. "What a dreadful thing to have upon my tombstone—'Defeated by pigs'—I, who beat both the Indians and the Redcoats!" He turned his face to the wall and from that moment on grew steadily worse.

The days went by and no others came to try their luck at the reward. Even the notice that Betsy had copied out so beautifully tore loose from the post where it had been nailed and was blown away in a high wind. It surely did look as though this were the end of General Billycock.

It would be pleasing to record that as he weakened his disposition grew sweeter, but it was not so. His voice, though faint, spoke no kinder words than before, and with what strength was left to him he fumed and fretted at his family and servants who tended to him—all except Betsy, of course.

Now Betsy was terribly grieved by the General's decline, for she loved her father dearly despite his bluster and bullying ways. She stayed in the sickroom reading to him and waiting on him as much as her mother would allow. When she was not there she was in the kitchen making tarts and custards to tempt the General's poor appetite. Although she was very young she was very clever.

One day the little girl appeared looking so pale and droopy that her mother declared they would soon have another patient in the house if she were not sent outdoors into the sunshine and fresh air for a time. She ordered a servant to fetch round Miss Betsy's mare and instructed her daughter to go for a nice brisk ride.

Obediently Betsy put on her plum-colored riding habit and set out on the little white mare, Liberty, which her father had given her. It was a beautiful day, clear and bright and mild. The hills of Tennessee stood up blue under the sun and shifting clouds. Betsy had always been told never to ride far from the settlement and especially never to go alone into the forest, but the little girl had been so long in the big stone house with the gloom of sickness that she cantered along, forgetting everything except the pleasure of motion and the wind blowing in her curls. She did not even pay any attention to the pigs, who looked

26

up from their rooting in the young peach orchard and grunted disagreeably as she rode by.

She rode for a long time, in a sort of daydream. The trees became taller and closer together, and great stretches of bare rock rang under the hoofs of the small mare, who slowed to an ambling walk. Presently Betsy came to herself and realized that she was indeed in the forest and climbing steadily upward on some sort of faint trail. Still she didn't turn back, for the humming of the insects and the piping of the birds all around her seemed very friendly and she saw nothing to be afraid of. The sun was high and she was certain that she could easily find her way back. So she rode on up the mountainside until, suddenly, she heard a clear voice singing

"Rolly tudum tudum
Rolly tudum day,"

and around a great boulder as high as a house Betsy came upon a boy not much older than herself. He was sitting on an old fallen tree, singing and studying a bit of tattered paper which he held in his hands. He looked up sharply as she reined in Liberty, who, prick-eared, had jumped a foot or two sideways at seeing him sitting there.

The boy was dressed in jacket and leggings of deerskin. His hair was yellow and rough and his eyes were a light bright gray in his thin brown face. He smiled and said "Howdy, Ma'am."

Betsy was mightily pleased; she had always been called Betsy or Miss Betsy or just Miss. No one had ever called her "Ma'am" before—it made her feel very grown up.

"How do you do, boy?" she answered grandly. "I am Miss Betsy Billycock, the General's daughter. What is your name and what are you reading?"

"My name is Dion Fayreweather, Miss Betsy Billycock, Ma'am, and I'm reading—or trying to, for I've not had all the schooling I might—a bit of paper I found stuck in a holly tree over yonder. The writing is surely the prettiest I've ever seen and I think I can read the name Billycock as plain as plain. Would it be about yourself, Miss Betsy, Ma'am?"

At this, Betsy got down from her saddle and went to sit on the log beside Dion Fayreweather to see what the paper might be that had Billycock on it. Why, it was the notice that she had copied out for her father—the one that had been nailed up on the post in the settlement until it blew away in a high wind!

Betsy read the notice to Dion and explained the whole story of the pigs and her father's illness. It appeared that the boy and his family lived back on the mountain and came down very seldom to the settlement in the valley.

"That's a sad story, Miss Betsy, Ma'am," said Dion when she had finished. "I reckon there's nothing I can do that hasn't been tried and failed, but I do know of an old Indian wise man—a shaman, he's called. He lives by himself on the mountaintop up there, and while most settlers put no store on what a red man says, still he told my pa where a hurt hound was lying that had took on a mountain cat. He told my ma to look in the butter churn for her lost locket—there it was!—and he cured my littlest brother of fits. It might be that he'd know of a way to rid your pa of pigs!"

"Oh, Dion!" cried Betsy, clasping her hands and forgetting to be grand. "If only he could! Would you show me how to find this old man? I'd do anything to help my poor father, and if the Indian cures him there will be gold and silver for you, too, as the paper there says."

"Why, I'll take you to the shaman and gladly, Miss Betsy, and not just for gold and silver," Dion answered gallantly. "Ride your pony up a piece to our cabin and then we must climb the rest of the way ourselves for it's too steep and rocky for a horse."

So Betsy got back on Liberty and Dion led the little mare up a twisty path until they came to a log cabin set in a clearing against the mountainside. There was a large black kettle bubbling away over a fire in the yard, and several small children, a number of chickens, and some big and little hounds were roving about at a safe distance from it. They all set up a great clamor as Betsy and Dion came along, and a tall, thin woman in a gray homespun dress appeared at the cabin door.

"Come running, Ma!" called Dion. "Here's Miss Betsy Billy-cock that I met down the mountain a piece. Her pa is a general and he's took bad with pigs! We're just going up to see if the shaman has a cure for them. Could you give us a cup of milk and a corn cake before we start?"

"Indeed, yes!" cried the tall, thin woman, running down the steps into the yard to help Betsy from the saddle. She pushed back the little girl's dark tangled hair and looked deep into Betsy's eyes. Her own eyes were like Dion's—a light bright gray —and her hair, which at first sight Betsy had thought gray also, was a faded yellow.

"My! My! A general's daughter! I never thought to have such an honor in my life!" she said, smiling. "Light down, sweeting, and set a spell before you go. If it's any help you need, the old shaman is a likely man. Many laugh at the Indians and call them ignorant, but the shaman up there is as wise a man as ever I saw. You mustn't be frightened of him, though he is very old and speaks little. He's a good man and will help you if he's able."

Inside the clean, bare cabin Betsy and Dion each had a cup of milk and a corn cake while Dion's mother hovered over them, and the hounds and younger children sat around begging as though they had never been fed in their lives. Betsy was so charmed by her new friends and so excited at the prospect of visiting the shaman and perhaps curing her father, she never gave a thought to the time. She had quite forgotten her promise not to ride far. Very blithely she got up and said good-by to Dion's mother, thanking her with a neat curtsey.

"Mind you take good care of the General's daughter," Dion's mother called after them, waving her apron. "Don't let her slip upon the rocks and keep an eye out for snakes!"

The two children set off on foot up the mountainside, leaving the white mare Liberty tied to a picket in the cabin yard. It was a long, steep climb over rocks and logs and tree roots and slippery pine needles. The trailing skirt of Betsy's riding habit got much in her way and several times she would have fallen had not Dion grabbed her hand. Both children were hot and breathless when at last they came out upon a vast, bare outcropping of rock at the crest of the mountain. There they sat down awhile to rest.

Betsy had never been so high before. Born in the valley below, she had never been on top of the mountains for the roads were few and poor and traveling was dangerous for women and children. She now looked out amazed over the whole valley to the rows of more mountains beyond, bluer and bluer in the distant haze. There was the wide, rolling Tennessee like a great shining snake, and there was the little settlement with its handful of buildings and its clearings. There, even, was her father's big stone house set upon its green knoll, and she thought she could see black specks in the spaces about it that must be the pigs!

Betsy would like to have stayed there a long time but Dion soon leaped up and said that they must hurry on to see the shaman if they were to get down the treacherous path again before dusk. They went on, slowly and cautiously, along a high, rocky ledge. Betsy was so occupied with keeping her footing on the loose and slippery stone that she didn't see the shaman until Dion whispered, "There he is!" stopping so suddenly that Betsy bumped into the boy. She peered over Dion's shoulder.

The shaman was sitting silent and motionless on the ledge in front of a dark cave mouth. He looked very old and frail; his face and hands were like withered oak leaves and his hair was thin and white. He sat wrapped in a great black bear robe, staring out over the valley with half-shut eyes.

"Does he live here all alone?" Betsy whispered to Dion, and the boy whispered back, nodding.

"His people have mostly moved on westward but he wouldn't go. Nobody knows how old he is, or how he manages to get food. Some say the wild animals and birds bring it to him; some say he conjures it out of the wind. Most folks around these parts have never even heard of him, or pay no mind if they have. He doesn't talk much, but once he showed me some carved horn and bits of broken clay bowls that he said had belonged to

people who lived in these caves long before his tribe came here.''

Now Dion moved up to stand in front of the old Indian wise man, who had not turned his head or made any sign that he knew the children were there. Betsy waited, a little fearfully.

"I greet you, shaman,'' Dion said in a formal way, not smiling. "Here is a daughter of the white war chief who lives in the great stone lodge in the valley. She comes to ask a boon. Hear her, Shaman.''

For a minute Betsy thought that the old man had not heard or else that he just wasn't going to answer. Then, slowly, he turned his head and looked straight at her. His eyes, glistening out of the brown web of wrinkles, heavy-lidded and veiled, reminded her of a turtle's eyes. Although he didn't smile, there was something very good in his face that reassured the little girl. When the shaman spoke she thought of faraway winds, distant but strong.

"Draw near, Daughter of White War Chief. I have waited for you all day. Speak."

Betsy was amazed. Had he really known she was coming? Shyly she stammered out the story of her father and the pigs. When she finished, the old man was silent, staring at her, but she thought that she saw a smile around his wrinkled mouth. The two children waited, and presently the shaman spoke again.

"Tell your father, the White War Chief, that bad spirits are drawn to bad spirits. When he drives out the pigs within him so will those that trouble his lands depart."

"Oh!" cried Betsy, wringing her hands and imagining what the General would say to that! "Isn't there something more that we can do?"

In answer the old Indian once again gazed out across the distances with eyes that seemed no longer aware of the children.

"Come," whispered Dion, tugging at Betsy's hand. "That's all. He will say no more. We must go." They went away, leaving the shaman just as they had found him.

When they got back to the cabin, Dion's father was there with a mess of gray squirrels slung over his shoulder by a deer-skin thong, and his long rifle on his arm. He was a tall, lanky man, sandy-haired and blue-eyed, and the younger children and the hound pups jumped noisily about him, trying to reach the squirrel tails. He bowed very awkwardly to Betsy's curtsey but his smile was wide and warm.

"What did the shaman say? Did he help you?" asked Dion's mother, shooing at the children and puppies with her apron.

37

Betsy looked doubtful. She repeated what the old Indian had said.

"Lawk-a-mercy!" cried Dion's mother. "What a curious notion! Pigs inside! I never! Still the shaman talks in riddles sometimes. I'm sure that he meant you well. Best do as he told you, strange though it be. Now come in, sweeting, and have a bit of supper before you go. Then my husband will see you safely down the trail."

At that Betsy realized for the first time how long she had been away and how far she had wandered from home.

"Oh, dear! Oh, dear!" she cried, "they will have the whole settlement out searching for me! Poor Mamma, she has enough to fret her as it is. I must go immediately!"

So Dion's mother kissed her and tucked some johnnycake into the pocket of her riding coat. Dion's father lifted her onto Liberty's back and, taking the reins, set off down the trail which was already dusky with long shadows. Dion walked behind. Before the cabin passed from sight, Betsy turned in the saddle and waved to Dion's mother, who stood with the young children and the hounds and the chickens around her. The chickens were clucking, looking hopefully for their evening ration of grain. The hounds bayed and yapped, excited by the goings-on of the day. The children and their mother called,

"Good-by! Good-by, Miss Betsy Billycock! Come again soon."

Dion and his father stayed with Betsy until there was nothing but an open field between her and the big stone house.

"I don't see any signs of excitement," said Betsy, looking

toward her home. "Perhaps they've all been so busy with poor Papa that I've not been missed. Oh, dear, those horrid pigs are even closer than when I left—see, they are right up in the rose arbor!"

"Are you going to tell your father tonight what the shaman said?" asked Dion.

Betsy answered, sighing, "I suppose I must. One must try what one can. Still, you have no idea of poor, dear Papa's temper. He doesn't like Indians to begin with, and when I tell him that one said he has pigs inside— Oh, dear! Oh, dear!"

She thanked her new friends and set off at a canter toward home but when she drew near the stable she slowed Liberty to a walk. Quietly, quietly they entered the stable. Old Cannon-ball looked over his stall, where he had been sulking most of the time since the General spurred him. The wagon team also saw them come in, and so did the stable cat. There were no humans about. Betsy slipped into the big house and up the stairs to her own room where she quickly changed her riding habit for a muslin dress.

When she reached her father's room it was just as she had thought—no one had missed her. The General had had such a bad day that every member of the household had been busy trying to please him.

"Here I am, Mamma dear—all fresh and rested," said Betsy, entering. "Now all of you go away and I will sit with Papa."

With little persuasion General Billycock's wife and sons and servants left the room, exhausted by their day with the ailing General, and happy to escape for a while. Betsy drew up a rush-

bottom chair to her father's bedside and settled herself in it. She
eyed the General carefully. He looked very bad indeed—very ill
and very bad-tempered.

"I am sorry that you have had such a dreadful day, dear
Papa," she began, patting his hand, which lay limply on the
quilt, "Mamma made me go for a ride on Liberty and I did have
a very pleasant time—as pleasant as I could," she added quickly,
"knowing how ill you are."

General Billycock groaned feebly.

"I rode quite a long way," Betsy continued, "farther than I
should, I fear. I went right up the mountainside before I was
at all aware of it. But just as I was about to turn around and ride
home I met a most pleasant boy. His name is Dion Fayreweather
and he lives with his family in a cabin on the mountain. He
invited me there and his mother gave me milk and cake. His
father is a woodsman."

Alarm showed in the General's pale blue eyes. "Mustn't—go
trafficking with—strangers," he wheezed weakly. "Very—dangerous. Did—you come—straight—down again?"

"Well—no, Papa dear, not *straight* down again," replied
Betsy in her most winning manner, patting away at the General's hand. "You see, they told me, the Fayreweathers did, of—
of—someone they knew about who lived farther up the mountain. They said he might help you feel better and get rid of those
dreadful pigs. This someone is very wise and has helped the
Fayreweathers many times. Dion took me to see him. I talked
to him and then I came straight home. Dion and his father
brought me down to the open fields."

40

General Billycock had closed his eyes. "I—no longer—look for help," he sighed feebly, "but—who is—this person, and—what—did he say? Of course—he—can't help—me."

Betsy took a deep breath and raised her eyes to heaven.

"He's a wise man. A shaman, he's called. You know—an Indian."

General Billycock's eyes flew open with some semblance of their old pop. A faint shade of brick-dust color tinged his pale and wasted cheeks.

"A—a—a—an Indian?" he croaked. "Surely, child, not—a—an *Indian!* What—do—*Indians* know? What—rubbish—did—he tell—you?"

"Now, Papa dear, please don't excite yourself," Betsy pleaded. "He was really most kind and polite and I'm certain he could help you if only you . . ."

"What—*did*—he—say?" insisted her father, just managing to raise his head a bare half-inch off the pillow.

"He said—" Betsy faltered, then she clasped her hands tightly together, sat up very straight, and tossed her head. "Very well, Papa dear, he said that if you wanted to get well and get rid of the pigs outside you must first get rid of the pigs inside yourself. There!"

General Billycock's fingers plucked feverishly at the quilt.

"He said—that Indian said—that—that I —that—"

Betsy looked straight into her father's wildly rolling eyes. She removed the bedspread from his fingers and tucked it firmly under his chin. She said very calmly and very clearly:

"That Indian said that you have pigs inside, Papa, and really, dearest Papa, so you have. If you want to get well and not have pigs outside on the lawn, you simply must be pleasanter and kinder and more considerate and more agreeable to everyone!"

And then she burst into tears.

She cried and she cried.

"Don't!" croaked her father, very much alarmed, for Betsy was not a weepy child and, in fact, he had not seen her cry since she was a baby. "Don't—pray don't—"

But Betsy cried on and on.

"You won't even try—I know you won't!" she wailed with her hands over her face. "There, I've gone all alone up the mountain and among strangers and wild beasts, clambering over rocks and along dangerous ledges to see an old Indian, all to help you, and you don't care a bit!"

Now, hard and ill-tempered as General Billycock was, it

troubled him to see Betsy cry. Also, it challenged his old fighting spirit to be told that he wouldn't try. So after many tears and much argument he agreed to try to be pleasanter, kinder, more considerate, and more agreeable. But he did not want anyone to laugh at him for taking an Indian's advice, so it was to be a secret between himself and Betsy.

There was one favorable thing to be said of General Billycock—when he set himself to a task he was not halfhearted about it. So, old soldier that he was, he started out to be pleasant, kind, and agreeable as though he were charging into battle.

That evening he frightened all his household by saying "Please" and "Thankee" and "Quite all right" so determinedly that they were certain that he was preparing for his last hour and they sat up all that night with shawls over their night clothes, weeping and waiting for the end of General Billycock.

Only Betsy went calmly off to sleep. Early the next morning she jumped up out of her curtained cherry bed and ran to the window. The pigs were still there but it seemed to her hopeful eyes that they were a bit farther from the house than they had been the day before and they were not rooting and shoveling with quite so much enthusiasm.

Also, when General Billycock awoke he looked better, and when Betsy whispered in his ear the news about the pigs, his eyes almost sparkled.

For the next several days General Billycock was pleasant, kind, and considerate with a great determination. When he smiled, which was often—a thing he had never used to do—he showed all his teeth in a really frightening manner, and his agreeableness upset his household almost as much as his disagreeableness had done!

Every day now the pigs withdrew a little farther from the house, some of them no longer rooting at all but just standing about looking rather poorly. Every day General Billycock grew a little stronger and looked a little better. Soon he was able to leave his bed and sit in the wing chair by the window. What the General was doing was still a secret between himself and Betsy and they rejoiced together over his success.

"Ha, ha!" cried General Billycock, showing all his teeth in a ferociously agreeable smile. "Ha, ha! I'll teach 'em, the nasty beasts! Thought they had the best of General Billycock, did they! Ha, ha!"

Then one day, as all was going so nicely, the servant girl bringing General Billycock his high tea tripped on a wrinkle in the rug and spilled the pudding to which he had been looking forward with much pleasure.

General Billycock's face turned the old familiar shade of purple. His pale blue eyes popped and his ginger hair stood on end. He began to rant and rave and throw whatever he could lay his hands on—slippers, pillows, and books, candlesticks and snuffers. The servant girl fled terrified. So did the rest of the household—all except Betsy, who did what she could to calm her raging father. But the General would not be calmed. All the bad temper that he had bottled up for the past days came roaring out in one terrific fit!

He was boiling away like a hot pot of hominy when there was a sound of sharp, running feet and a large dark shape appeared in the doorway of his room. Betsy shrieked!

44

General Billycock turned pale and fell back into his wing chair, clutching the arms.

The big black boar staring in at them with squinty little red eyes grinned as only mean pigs can grin. "Hoo!" it snuffled, dribbling dirt from its ugly snout all over the polished floor.

General Billycock could neither move nor speak he was so frightened. Betsy was frightened also, but she was a brave little girl so she took up the bright brass poker from the chimney corner and began to beat on the black boar.

"Get out!" she cried. "Get away and leave Papa alone, you horrid thing!"

The pig did as she said, turning and lumbering down the stairs and out of the house just as it had come. Its parting look, though, was as threatening as words.

"Never mind, Papa dear," Betsy said soothingly to the General who, to her amazement, had burst into tears and was blubbering away like a great, stout, ginger-haired baby. "The pigs shan't harm you. I won't let them."

Even as she said this she saw to her dismay through the window that all the pigs had returned and were rooting away with a vengeance right under the walls of the house.

"Ow—ow—ow—ow—ow!" wept General Billycock. "It's no use! The creatures will come back! I'm done for! I'm a hateful, mean, hard, ill-tempered old man. I see it now. But I've been a hateful, mean, hard, ill-tempered old man so long that I don't know how to be anything else! I don't know how to change! Ow—ow—ow—ow—ow—ow!"

The General's family and servants now timidly returned, brought by his wails, and Betsy slipped away, unable to bear the sad scene any longer. She ran out of the house, past the pigs, and down the lawn to the bank where the willow trees leaned over the waters of the wide-rolling Tennessee. There she sat down and put her head on her knees.

She sat there for a long time while the sun sank lower and lower, wondering what to do, until a voice said,

"Good evening to you, Miss Betsy Billycock, Ma'am."

It was, of course, Dion Fayreweather. He had a long pole in his hand and a string of fish over his shoulder.

"I came down to the valley today for a bit of fishing and, having caught enough for the pan, I'd a mind to stop and see how you and your pa were faring."

Betsy was relieved to have someone to tell her sad story to.

"I fear there's nothing to be done now," she said sorrowfully. "Poor Papa has always had a dreadful temper and he is just

46

too old to change his ways now all by himself, although I truly believe that at last he would like to. Oh, if there were only some cure for bad temper!"

"Why, Miss Betsy," replied Dion, "there may be just such a thing! A couple of nights ago a pair of travelers stopped by the cabin to sleep and get directions from Pa. After supper, as we all sat around the fire singing and talking, they got to telling of a marvel man right over the mountain in the next settlement."

"A marvel man?" exclaimed Betsy. "Why, what does he do?"

"He just arrived a week ago in a Conestoga wagon from the eastern cities, so he says—Boston and New York and Philadelphia and Baltimore. There he amazed the people with his cures. He sells bottles of a marvelous medicine that is supposed to cure everything—warts, boils, falling hair, bunions, rheumatism, gout, stiffness, cracked hoofs in horses, sour milk in cows, and"—Dion's voice became low and impressive—"ill humors of all sorts in man and beast!"

"Oh, Dion!" cried Betsy, sitting bolt upright. "That is just what poor Papa needs! He is always in a dreadful ill humor! We must go immediately and get a bottle."

"But, Miss Betsy," Dion protested, "it's a good ten miles, with night coming on. Also, it costs a whole silver dollar to buy a bottle of the medicine!"

"No matter!" replied Betsy grandly. "I've a silver dollar all my own which my godmother in Virginia sent me for my birthday. By a traveling preacher she sent it—she said it would be a temptation to anyone else—and I can do as I like with it. I'll fetch it now and we'll start right away."

"Wouldn't it be better to send one of your brothers or a servant?" begged Dion, thinking of what the old General would say if he found out that his daughter had ridden over the mountain in the dead of night.

"Dear me, no!" said Betsy determinedly. "I want to go myself to help Papa, and besides, I have never been over the mountain before. It will be exciting! My brothers and the servants are all afraid of Cannonball, Papa's old war horse, and the wagon team is far too slow. If you are afraid to ride Cannonball, I will ride him myself, and you may have my pony, Liberty. Cannonball knows me quite well."

"Oh, I've a hand with horses," answered Dion stoutly, a little cross that the General's daughter should think herself braver than he. "Back in Carolina I often rode my grandpa's black stallion that no one else but the old man could handle. You've only to whisper in a horse's ear and he quiets right down. You'll see."

So while Betsy went to fetch the silver dollar and to change her gown for a riding habit, Dion went to the stable to ready the horses, taking great care that no one should see him. Cannonball, who had grown tired of sulking, was so pleased with the thought of going out that he gave no trouble while being bridled and saddled even though Dion was a stranger. When Betsy reached the stable, both horses were ready, and Dion helped her into Liberty's saddle. He then leaped upon Cannonball's back and the old war horse bucked and snorted, but the boy leaned forward and spoke in his ear, patting him, and the big roan became quite easy.

48

Quietly the children walked the horses away from sight of the house until they came to the road that led over the mountain, and then they began to gallop. It was only a wagon road, rough and deeply rutted. Once away from General Billycock's fields and the outskirts of the settlement, the tall, dark forest closed in on either side. The sun went down and the moon came up. It cast the horses' shadows before them and made old Cannonball plunge and shy. Owls hooted and answered one another, and bats swooped silently over the road. Once a panther screamed far off.

The two children galloped the horses awhile, then walked them, then galloped again. In some places the rise of the road was very steep and the horses had almost to scramble up. After about two hours they came over the mountain pass and saw the lights of the other settlement, and presently they were riding between the rough log buildings.

There were a surprising number of people about for that time of night for people in the frontier towns generally went to bed early and got up early. Many curious glances were turned

on the boy on the big roan horse and the girl in the fashionable habit on the white pony. Dion drew Cannonball up to ask a red-whiskered man where the marvel man was to be found. The man pointed to the end of the street where a crowd had gathered in front of a Conestoga wagon. The back opening of the wagon was outlined by lighted lanterns and a man standing under them leaned out and waved his arms, talking loudly. When Dion and Betsy got closer, they saw that he had a large bottle in one hand and beside him in the wagon was a table on which stood dozens of bottles just like the one he held.

"This has cured His Excellency, the French Ambassador, of a long-standing case of gout," he was saying in a theatrical voice, "and General Washington himself, our late-lamented President, begged for a bottle of this elixir on his deathbed. Alas, it did not reach him in time, else he would be with us yet, hale and hearty!"

The speaker was a small, dark man, very wiry and agile. He was dressed in a worn but elaborate suit of an older time—sky-blue knee breeches and coat, with a soiled "weskit" of lavender silk shot through with tarnished silver thread. Torn lace adorned his neck and spilled from under the large turned-back cuffs of his sleeves, and his dark hair was caught back at the nape with a black ribbon. As he talked his small, sharp eyes darted over the crowd of gapers before him.

"It is known to be beneficial for the bite of all poisonous varmints, reptile or insect. Cures boils, dissolves warts, grows hair, restores sight, and renders pure the system of any man or beast made noxious by evil humors!"

51

Betsy did not understand all that the little man was saying but at the mention of evil humors she urged Liberty forward through the crowd, showing her silver dollar and crying:

"One bottle, please, sir! I wish to purchase one bottle!"

"Aha!" said the little man, leaning far out from the wagon opening to peer closely at her, "here is a wise young gentlewoman in the bloom of health! Nothing like my elixir as a precaution. Taken by the young and whole they need never fear disease or the ravages of age. Here is your bottle, my dear. Just hand over your dollar."

"Oh, sir, it's not for myself," Betsy assured him, giving him the silver coin. "It's for my poor dear papa, who is sadly afflicted with pigs!"

The crowd guffawed, and someone at the edge of it muttered "Why, it's General Billycock's gal!"

"Pigs?" inquired the little man, wrinkling his brow. "Pigs? Ah, indeed. Pigs! Well, now, my dear, you will find that there is nothing better for livestock, swine or otherwise, than my elixir. It will produce the sweetest bacon, the tastiest ham that ever—"

"Oh, no, sir!" Betsy was about to explain when Dion pushed Cannonball up beside her and laid a hand on Liberty's rein.

"Come away, Miss Betsy, it doesn't matter what he thinks. It's late and we must hurry back." He glanced about uneasily at the faces in the lantern light. "There's some here whose looks I don't much care for."

The two children rode out of the crowd and down the rutted street to the edge of the settlement.

"Now, Miss Betsy Billycock, Ma'am," said Dion seriously, "let's gallop. The horses have been kept up so long, some hard riding will not hurt them."

The moon was waning as they galloped up the mountain pass. There was no sound except the drumming of the horses' hoofs on the hard road. Betsy felt very happy; she kept patting the bottle of elixir in her saddlebag. Then from the tall, dark pines two horsemen wheeled out, one from either side of the road. Liberty and Cannonball snorted and shied into each other, and Dion cried, "Look out, Miss Betsy!"

The children did their best to escape the trap but the two horsemen caught their bridle reins and pulled Liberty and Cannonball to a stop. In the fading moonlight Dion recognized the men as two he had seen back in the crowd. They were an evil-looking pair.

"Ha!" grinned the one holding Liberty's rein. "Reckon the ole Gineral will pay a fat purse to get this little partridge back safe! What'll we do with the boy?"

"Oh, tie him up and leave him in the woods," growled the other. "The horses will bring a pretty price farther down the river, especially this big roan."

Dion had drawn his long hunting knife, determined to do what he could to save Betsy and himself, but the ruffian horseman reached out a huge hand and, seizing Dion's wrist, twisted it until he had to drop the knife. Betsy, not saying a word, sat wide-eyed and fearful, clutching Liberty's mane. There seemed that nothing could save them, but Cannonball had not forgotten his days as a war horse.

Many a time the big roan had saved his master when the old General was sore beset by enemy horsemen all around him. Now Cannonball reached out and with his great square yellow teeth bit his captor so hard upon the knee that the man yelled and dropped his hold on Cannonball's rein. Then, quickly, the old war horse turned himself around and let go a kick that almost knocked the ruffian's horse right off his legs. It did just as well—it knocked the ruffian right off the horse!

Free, Dion rode Cannonball around behind the other ruffian who was holding Liberty's rein. But this man had seen what had happened to his companion. Before Cannonball's teeth or hoofs could reach him he dropped Liberty's rein and spurred his horse into the forest, leaving his companion still lying on the ground.

"Ride fast, Miss Betsy!" cried Dion, and the two children set their horses off at a dead run. Cannonball and Liberty, excited by the happenings and headed for home, did not slacken pace until they were in the stable yard. With a very few words Betsy and Dion parted. Betsy ran into the house and up the stairs while Dion put away the weary horses and took himself home to his own cabin.

"Here, Papa! Quickly! Drink this!" Betsy cried breathlessly, bursting into the General's room.

"What's that? Where have you been?" Her mother, brothers, and all the servants leaped from their places about General Billycock's bed and crowded around her.

"I've been to the marvel man over the mountain, and with my birthday dollar I bought this bottle of elixir. It will cure all evil humors in man or beast!"

Betsy pushed them aside and, uncorking the bottle, handed it to her father. Hope flickered in General Billycock's eyes. He reached out a feeble hand and, taking the bottle, he drained it to the very last drop.

"Thankee, m'dear," he said with a sigh, and promptly fell into a deep sleep that lasted all night.

56

The next morning a great change had come over General Billycock. He was quiet, he was pleasant. He said "Please" and "Thankee" and "Quite all right," and he said these agreeable things without grinning ferociously or ha-ha-ing loudly or triumphantly.

That day the pigs moved several feet away from the house.

The next day General Billycock was just as pleasant and just as quiet. He looked much better and seemed much stronger. The pigs moved even farther away and stood around dismally, hardly bothering to root at all.

The next day and the next day and the day after that General Billycock was quiet, pleasant, and stronger. The pigs moved away farther and farther and they rooted less and less. At the end of the week General Billycock was sitting in his wing chair all day, looking quite well indeed, and watching from his window the pigs who stood about on the edges of the fields, heads hanging low and tails limp.

Indeed, he felt so well that he sent for his manservant to bring the razor and the basin and shave him of the ginger whiskers that had sprouted on his cheeks and chin during his illness. Pleased at this certain sign of recovery, all the household gathered to watch.

The manservant arranged the linens under his master's chin and lathered him from the General's own mug. He sharpened the General's own razor and began to shave off the ginger whiskers. And then, because he was nervous, the manservant's hand trembled and with the sharp razor he nicked General Billycock's chin!

The manservant dropped the razor. The rest of the household gasped. Betsy put her hands over her face and peeped through her fingers. There was a dreadful silence.

Then General Billycock spoke.

"My good man," he said quietly and pleasantly, "I do believe

that you have nicked my chin. Kindly be more careful. Now pick up the razor and get on with the work, please."

Not another word was said. The shaving went on, but candles had to be brought in and lit before it was over because, although only the middle of the afternoon, the sky was growing very dark.

"There's going to be a storm," everyone said, running about the house, lowering windows. It grew darker and darker. The General, all shaven, sat by the window and watched the hills of Tennessee turning almost black under the stormy sky and the pigs moving about uneasily at the edges of the fields. More candles had to be brought. It was soon almost as dark as night.

There was a knock at the door and Dion came in, He had been coming down every day to inquire about the General, and General Billycock received the boy very kindly.

"Oh, what a storm there's brewing!" said Dion. "You can hear a great rumbling over the hills to the east. It sounds like a battle!"

They all went to stand by the window and watch the storm. And what they saw was a great black whirling funnel that came spinning down out of the eastern hills straight toward the house. It was as high as the sky, as black as night, and it came with a rush and a roar that bent the trees to the ground.

For an instant it seemed that it was going to strike the house, but it veered. Around the house it went, spinning like a top— once around, twice around—and as it went it sucked up the pigs who had scattered and were running wildly in all directions. Not a one escaped. Every single pig, big and small, was sucked up into that great whirling dark funnel, and when the last one

was caught, the funnel spun away, over the General's lands, over the settlement, over the wide, rolling waters of the Tennessee, over the forests beyond, and finally disappeared from sight across the mountains. When it was gone the sun came out and shone brightly on General Billycock's big square stone house.

The day after the pigs departed General Billycock had three bags filled up with gold and silver coins. One he gave to Dion who carried it home to his delighted family. One he sent by Dion to the old Indian shaman. The shaman, when he saw the bag of money, only smiled and shook his head, waving it away, so Dion took it down again to the General who insisted that Dion have that bag as well.

The third bag of money General Billycock sent over the mountain by Dion, mounted on Cannonball, with the General's own pistol, loaded and cocked, stuck in his belt. He was to deliver it to the marvel man in the next settlement.

Betsy was not allowed to go along on this journey but she rode out to meet Dion on the edge of her father's fields as he came riding back. He still had the money in his saddlebag and a strange tale to tell.

He had not been able to find the marvel man; the settlers told him that they had run the marvel man out of the settlement with the threat of a hanging if he ever returned. He had been caught, early in the morning following the children's visit, down on the banks of the Tennessee, filling his bottles with river water!

"Why, then," cried Betsy, "why, then—the elixir was nothing, after all! Nothing at all!"

"Only river water," replied Dion. "The marvel man was a fake."

"Then—how did it cure Papa?" asked Betsy.

"I don't know," answered Dion. "Maybe the bottle that you bought really had an elixir in it. Maybe the marvel man ran out

of elixir and decided to use river water to fool everyone."

"Yes," Betsy said, "or maybe Papa just believed it was going to cure him. Maybe he just cured himself."

"Maybe that's it," Dion agreed, plucking a long spear of grass and chewing on it thoughtfully. "I've heard tell that anything you believe in hard enough has a way of being so."

Of course, since the marvel man had disappeared they could never find out the truth.

And that was the end of General Billycock's pigs. They never returned to trouble him again and he remained pleasant, kind, considerate, and agreeable. If ever he was tempted to be otherwise he had only to remember those dreadful pigs.

Like the marvel man, the pigs were not seen again in that part of the country. But in later years settlers moving westward beyond the mountains of Tennessee found bands of wild pigs with tough hides and sharp, high backs. These they named "Razorback hogs" and they are still to be found in certain parts of Louisiana and Arkansas. Whether or not they are the descendants of General Billycock's pigs no one can truthfully say, but certainly they are very disagreeable creatures!